The Miracle at Jericho

BY MIIKO SHAFFIER
co-written by Chana Grosser

Illustrated by: Dmitry Gitelman (diemgi.com)
Layout & Design by: Ken Parker (visual-variables.com)

Published by:
Shefer Publishing
www.SheferPublishing.com

For permissions, comments and ordering information write:
Miiko@LearnHebrew.tv

ISBN 978-0-9978675-7-2

THE MIRACLE

AT JERICHO

an EASY EEVREET STORY

BY MIIKO SHAFFIER

SHEFER

PUBLISHING

Based on *Joshua, Chapter 6.*
Read this story like any English story book. When you get to a Hebrew word, do your best to sound it out and guess the meaning. You can check the pronunciation and meaning in the back of the book.

HAVE FUN!

Marching through the desert for forty years, the Israelites were free people with one G-d and no fears. Amazing miracles were in store for this nation. They were eager and excited to arrive at their destination.

As the Israelites approached the city of יְרִיחוֹ, they were not sure what to expect or what to do or even where to start. But they knew that G-d was on their side! It was time to conquer יְרִיחוֹ.

Inside יְרִיחוֹ the people felt prepared for any attack. Their עִיר was surrounded by a strong, unbreakable חוֹמָה. The gates to the עִיר were locked and barred. There was no one going out, and no one coming in.

G-d Himself spoke to יְהוֹשֻעַ son of NooN, the leader of the people of Israel: "Do not be afraid! You will enter יְרִיחוֹ. You will conquer it and defeat its king in a miraculous way."

"Walk around the חוֹמָה of the עִיר once each יוֹם. One יוֹם after another for 6 days. On the seventh יוֹם you will walk around the wall of the city שֶׁבַע times. And then a miracle will happen." G-d explained to יְהוֹשֻׁעַ exactly what to do.

First יְהוֹשֻׁעַ called the כֹּהֲנִים and said to them, "You will carry the Ark of the Covenant. Seven כֹּהֲנִים will walk ahead of the Ark, each carrying a שׁוֹפָר".

Then הוֹשֵׁעַ turned to the people of Israel: "You will all walk around the עִיר once. Pay attention: the Scouts will go first."

"Next the כֹּהֲנִים and the Ark, and then the people. The Rear Guard will come last."

On יוֹם רִאשׁוֹן, first thing in the morning, the people of Israel went to conquer יְרִיחוֹ.

יְרִיחוֹ was circled once.
Then everyone returned to the Israelite מַחֲנֶה.

They circled יְרִיחוֹ again on יוֹם שֵׁנִי
Then everyone returned again to the Israelite מַחֲנֶה.

The same thing happened on יוֹם שְׁלִישִׁי, and again on יוֹם רְבִיעִי. On יוֹם חֲמִישִׁי and on יוֹם שִׁשִּׁי too. Everyone marched one after the other. They marched in that same order and in perfect silence. Each יוֹם they circled יְרִיחוֹ once then returned to the מַחֲנֶה.

With יְהוֹשֻׁעַ in the lead
To influence and inspire,

Scouts ran up ahead
To know what would be required.

Seven כֹּהֲנִים marched
With a שׁוֹפָר each in hand.

The קֹדֶשׁ Ark followed
As they marched across the land.

Quiet, silent shhhhhh.
The people got in line.

The Rear Guard was last
And no one left behind.

This time after they circled the עִיר,
they did not return to their מַחֲנֶה.
Instead they circled יְרִיחוֹ a second time.
And then circled יְרִיחוֹ a third time. Around
and around they marched until they circled
יְרִיחוֹ six times!

Then the seventh time was different.

The כֹּהֲנִים blew their שׁוֹפָר making a tremendous sound. The people of Israel yelled and shouted!

As promised, a miracle happened in front of their eyes. The strong חוֹמָה of יְרִיחוֹ simply collapsed to the ground!

The Israelite army rushed in and conquered the עִיר.
And the miracle at יְרִיחוֹ was never forgotten.

Here are the Hebrew words from this *Easy Eevreet Story*:

יְרִיחוֹ   Y-ReeYCHoh - **JERICHO** |

עִיר   'eeYR - **CITY** |

חוֹמָה   CHohMahH - **WALL** |

יְהוֹשֻׁעַ   Y-HohSHoo'ah - **JOSHUA** |

יוֹם   YohM - **DAY** |

שֶׁבַע   SHehVah' - **SEVEN** |

כֹּהֲנִים   KohHahNeeYM - **PRIESTS** |

If it's only one priest use the word:

 כֹּהֵן   KohHehN - **PRIEST**

שׁוֹפָר   SHohFahR - **HORN** |

a type of trumpet made from a ram's horn

 **YohM Ree'SHohN – SUNDAY** | p. 15

YohM means day and Ree'SHohN means first. YohM Ree'SHohN is Sunday.

 **KohDehSH – HOLY** | p. 16,21

 **MahCHahNehH – CAMP** | p. 17,18,19,22

 **YohM SHehNeeY – MONDAY** | p. 18

YohM means day and SHehNeeY means second. YohM SHehNeeY is Monday.

 **YohM SH-LeeYSHeeY – TUESDAY** | p. 19

YohM means day and SH-LeeYSHeeY means third. YohM SH-LeeYSHeeY is Tuesday.

 **YohM R-VeeY'eeY – WEDNESDAY** | p. 19

YohM means day and R-VeeY'eeY means fourth. YohM R-VeeY'eeY is Wednesday.

 **YohM CHahMeeYSHeeY – THURSDAY** | p. 19

YohM means day and CHahMeeYSHeeY means fifth. YohM CHahMeeYSHeeY is Thursday.

 YohM SHeeSHeeY - **FRIDAY** | p. 19

YohM means day and SHeeSHeeY means sixth. YohM SHeeSHeeY is Friday.

 ShahBahT - **SATURDAY** | p. 20

The only day which has a unique name is SHahBahT, which means rest because SHahBahT is the day of rest.

 ZahHahV - **GOLD** | p. 25

 KehSehF - **SILVER** | p. 25

In Israel today, KehSehF can also mean money.

This story talks about the days of the week and numbers. In Hebrew we see that the days of the week are called First Day, Second Day, Third Day etc.

If you want to count like one, two, three etc. use these words:

1 אֶחָד
'ehCHahD

2 שְׁתַּיִם
SH-TahYeeM

3 שָׁלוֹשׁ
SHahLohSH

4 אַרְבַּע
'ahR-Bah'

5 חָמֵשׁ
CHahMehSH

6 שֵׁשׁ
SHehSH

7 שֶׁבַע
SHehVah'

8 שְׁמוֹנָה
SH-MohNahH

9 תֵּשַׁע
TehSHah'

10 עֶשֶׂר
'ehSehR

Now you know so many awesome Hebrew words! You can use your Hebrew words around the house or with friends. It'll be fun to tell your friend which יוֹם it is, or how much כֶּסֶף you have.

Hi!

My name is **Miiko**. I live in Be'er Sheva, Israel. My husband Aaron and I have nine kids: Menucha, Mendel, Dovi, Yisroel, Freida, Devora, Fitche, Geula, and Azaria.

I teach Hebrew reading with a fun little book called *Learn to Read Hebrew in 6 Weeks!*

My second book *The Hebrew Workbook* teaches readers to write in Hebrew.

The Miracle at Jericho is part of a series of storybooks that teach Hebrew vocabulary to kids.

I'm so pleased to be a part of your Hebrew journey. If you have any questions or want to say hi please send me an email!
Miiko@LearnHebrew.tv

To the Parents

This book is designed to teach Hebrew vocabulary to people who already know how to read the Hebrew alphabet. While reading this Bible story in English you'll come across Hebrew words embedded in the text. Sound out the words and try to guess their meaning from the context. Check the key in the back of the book to see if you were right.

I've chosen to transliterate the names of the biblical characters mentioned in this story so that you'll learn the authentic Hebrew pronunciation of these biblical names.

Transliteration

The Miracle at Jericho uses the same system of transliteration as my first book *Learn to Read Hebrew in 6 Weeks!*

I came up with a unique transliteration system. It's designed to have the reader pronouncing the Hebrew words accurately without ever having heard a Hebrew speaker pronounce those words.

Here's a breakdown of the system:

Each consonant is represented as a capital letter and each vowel by small letters.

The silent letters 'ahLehF (א) and 'ahYeeN (ע) are represented by an apostrophe (')

The silent vowel 'Sh-Vah' (ְ) is represented as a hyphen (-).

An important exception to make note of:
The CH does not represent the ch sound like in *chair* or *chest*. In fact, Hebrew doesn't have the ch sound like *chair* or *chest* at all.

The CH represents the letters CHehT(ח) and CHahF(כ) and Final ChahF(ך). These letters make a sound not found in the English language. It's a chokey sound that almost sounds like a kitten purring but much harsher. Think about the name of the composer Bach. From what my Spanish speaking students tell me, it's the same sound as the guttural J in Spanish.

Let's look at the first word in the Hebrew Scripture as an example of how my system works:

בְּרֵאשִׁית

I transliterate it:
B-Reh'SHeeYT

Others may transliterate Bereshit or Bresheet but then you wouldn't know if the vowels are long or short.

If you learned to read Hebrew using my other book, you are already well familiar with this system. But in case you learned to read Hebrew elsewhere, here's a key to make sure it's clear.

LEARN TO READ AND WRITE HEBREW WITH MY FUN AND EASY SYSTEM!

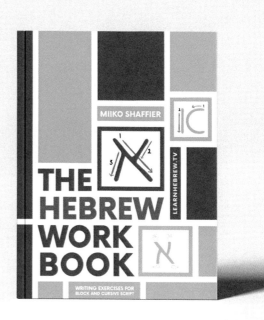

#1 BESTSELLERS
IN HEBREW LANGUAGE INSTRUCTION

- FUN MEMORY TRICKS
- 12 SIMPLE LESSONS
- PACED TO FINISH IN 6 WEEKS
- LEARN TO READ THE HEBREW BIBLE
- GREAT FOR ADULTS OR CHILDREN ALIKE
- CHARMING ILLUSTRATIONS TO MAKE LEARNING HEBREW A PLEASURE

MORE DETAILS AT LEARNHEBREW.TV

AVAILABLE AT AMAZON

Made in the USA
Middletown, DE
28 March 2023

27824551R00022